Hello Kitty

Annual 2014

© 1976, 2013 SANRIO CO., LTD.

ISBN: 978-0-00-751995-8

1 3 5 7 9 10 8 6 4 2

Text by Kirsty Neale

First published in the UK by HarperCollins *Children's Books* in 2013

www.harpercollins.co.uk

Printed and bound in China.

HarperCollins *Children's Books*

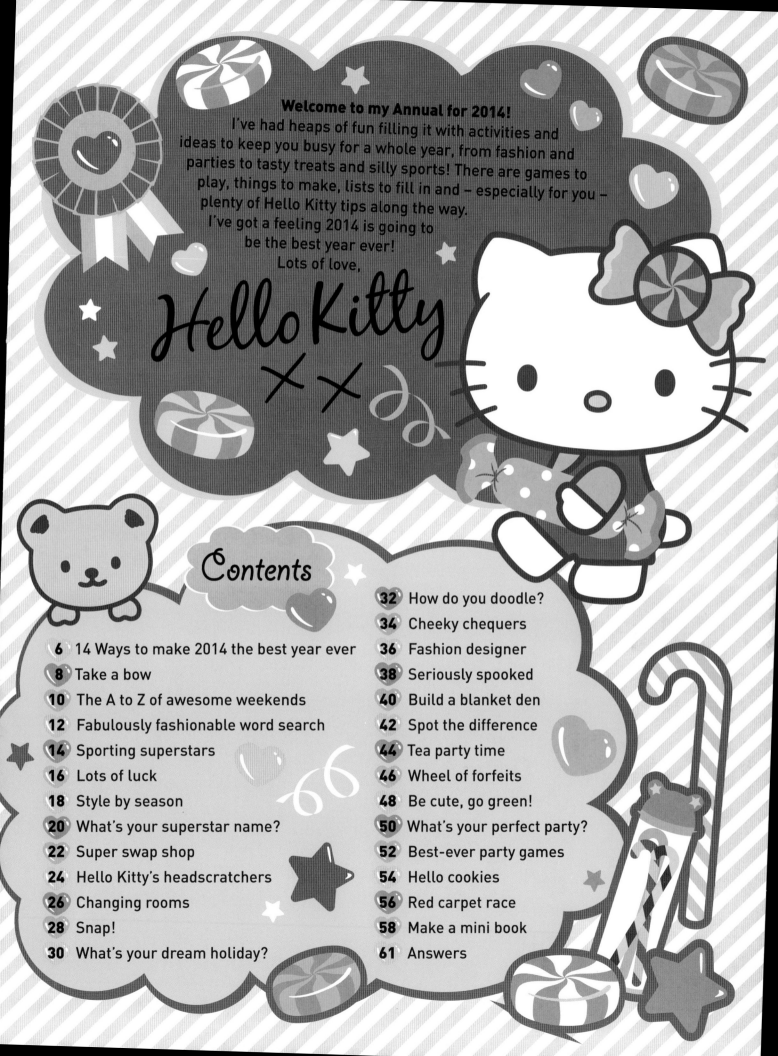

Welcome to my Annual for 2014!
I've had heaps of fun filling it with activities and ideas to keep you busy for a whole year, from fashion and parties to tasty treats and silly sports! There are games to play, things to make, lists to fill in and – especially for you – plenty of Hello Kitty tips along the way.
I've got a feeling 2014 is going to be the best year ever!
Lots of love,

Hello Kitty
xx

Contents

14 Ways to make 2014 the best year ever

This is my list of ideas for making 2014 totally amazing. Write out your own list on the next page – I'd love to know what you're planning!

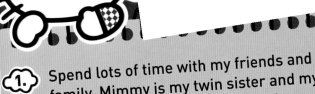

1. Spend lots of time with my friends and family. Mimmy is my twin sister and my friend, so she's doubly awesome!
2. Go on great family days out in the summer holidays. Take my diary and camera along so I remember every last minute.
3. Learn to play a new musical instrument. Shall I pick the violin, trumpet or drums?
4. Borrow a pile of brilliant books from the library every month.
5. Plan a totally fun joint birthday party with Mimmy.
6. Do something kind every day. Being nice to other people, even in the smallest way, makes me feel good, too!
7. Practise playing netball, so I may get picked for the school team. Woo-hoo!
8. Start a fun collection. Maybe postcards, stickers, badges . . . it's so hard to decide!
9. Dream up the best fancy dress costume for Halloween.
10. Invite my friends over for at least one amazing sleepover.
11. Try out some new sandwich flavours, so my school lunches are more interesting.
12. Do my homework as soon as I get in, so I can spend the rest of the day having fun!
13. Make friendship bracelets for all my pals, so they know how special they are.
14. Pick out a gorgeous dress and go to the school dance with Dear Daniel. He's such a good dancer!

Hello Kitty xx

Your turn!

1.

2.

3.

4.

5.

6.

7.

8.

9.

10.

11.

12.

13.

14.

Take a bow

Have you noticed I love bows? I wear them nearly all the time. If you'd like one of your own, check out this super-simple project, along with my top tips on how to wear your beautiful bow!

Templates

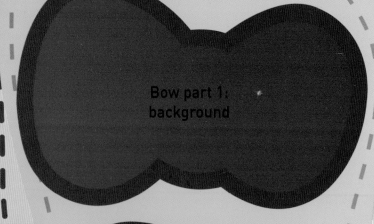

Bow part 1: background

Bow part 2: detail

Bow part 3: centre

You will need:

* ★ Tracing paper or thin plain paper
* ★ Pencil or felt-tip pen
* ★ Scissors
* ★ Felt

What to do:

1. Trace the three template pieces on to paper, then cut each one out.
2. Place the bow background on a piece of felt, and draw around it.
3. Cut out the felt shape, snipping just inside the outline.
4. Repeat steps 2 and 3 to cut out the bow centre and detail pieces.
5. Take your three felt pieces and spread glue over the back of the bow detail. Press it down neatly into the middle of the background piece.
6. Spread glue over the back of the bow centre, and press it down on top of the other two pieces.

Tip: Hold the paper template firmly in place with your other hand so it doesn't move as you draw around the outline.

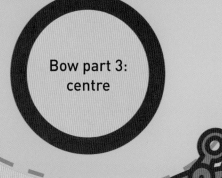

Ta-da!

Your bow is finished. Now take a look at these cool ideas and decide how you want to use it.

★ Spread some glue over the back of the bow, just in the centre part. Press it down on to a hair slide or Alice band. Allow the glue to dry, then wear it in your hair – just like me!

★ Glue your bow over the top of a flat buckle to give an old or boring belt a super-cute new look.

★ Try photocopying – or just drawing – the template pieces in different sizes to make bigger or smaller bows. I made a giant-sized version to hang on my bedroom door.

★ No felt? No problem! Make your bow from paper instead, and use it to decorate a plain notebook.

★ Turn your bow into a brooch, so you can wear it wherever you like. Glue a safety pin to the back or stick the bow on top of an old badge. Clip on to a cute cardigan, jacket, or even your school bag.

Tip: Look out for sparkly felt, or glue some glitter on your finished bow, to give it a gorgeously glam look.

The A to Z of awesome weekends

Saturday and Sunday are my favourite days of the week. Sometimes, there are so many cool things to do, I don't know where to start! Here's a list of my favourite weekend activities. Tick the box next to each one to show whether you've already done it (yay!), or want to give it a try.

Younger Hello Kitty fans should always get permission from a parent or guardian before doing any of the outdoor activities.

	Weekend activities	Already done it	Try this soon	Maybe one day
A	Get **ARTY**! Paint someone's portrait, learn to draw cartoons or tear up some old magazines and make a cool collage.			
B	Go **BOWLING**! The bowling alley is one of my favourite places to visit. Mimmy and I even made our own bowling pins from plastic water bottles so we can practise at home. Strike!			
C	Try **CHEERLEADING**! It doesn't matter whether you do it at a big match or just shake your pom-poms at home, cheering for your favourite sports team is tons of fun.			
D	Shall we **DANCE**? Some weekends I go to a ballet or tap class, but it's just as much fun making up dance moves in my bedroom with Mimmy and our friends.			
E	**ENTERTAIN** your family and friends! Whether it's singing, dancing, acting or even performing magic tricks, I can't get enough of putting on shows!			
F	Play **FRISBEE**! I love hanging out in the park, and seeing how far I can throw a Frisbee is one of my favourite things to do there.			
G	Give yourself a **GORGEOUS MAKEOVER**! Invite a few friends over and have fun dressing up, piling on accessories and giving each other fabulous new hairstyles.			
H	Have a go at **HORSE-RIDING**! One day I'd like my own horse, but for now, I'm happy visiting our local riding stables.			
I	**INVENT** something! It could be anything, from a new recipe to a cute way of stopping your socks falling down. Work out what you want, then invent it!			
J	Make your own **JEWELLERY**! I love stringing beads together to make necklaces and bracelets, or knotting pretty friendship bands from thread and ribbon.			
K	Let's go fly a **KITE**! It's best on windy weekends, but you can still have heaps of fun even if it's just breezy.			

	Weekend activities	Already done it	Try this soon	Maybe one day
L	Learn a foreign **LANGUAGE**! I love visiting other countries and it's even more fun if you understand what everyone is saying.			
M	Who's up for a **MOVIE MARATHON**? Grab a pile of your favourite DVDs, then invite your friends over! Make sure you've got plenty of comfy cushions and tasty snacks.			
N	Check out the **NIGHT SKY**. Star-gazing is awesome! I love looking into the sky trying to spot planets and count stars.			
O	Go **OUTDOORS**! Lots of the best weekend adventures happen outside. Family walks and nature trails are brilliant.			
P	**POST** something special to someone special. Write a letter, make a card, take a photo or draw a special picture. Package it up and send it off to someone you love.			
Q	Be **QUEEN FOR A DAY**! This is silly but lots of fun! Dress up in your fanciest dress, put on a tiara (or sparkly hairband) and ask everyone to call you 'your majesty'.			
R	Record your own **RADIO SHOW**! Our computer has a microphone, which makes it really easy to record your own voice and music.			
S	Go **SKATING**! From cute boots to the cool music they play at the rink, skating is the most fun you're ever likely to have falling over.			
T	Try **TRAMPOLINING**! Papa sometimes takes Mimmy and me to the trampoline at our local leisure centre. It's so cool to practise our favourite tricks.			
U	**UPDATE** your wardrobe! Get crafty and customise some of your old clothes to give them a whole new look. I especially love turning old jeans into cute shorts.			
V	Plant a **VEGGIE GARDEN**! My favourite things are carrots, strawberries, potatoes, peas and herbs. Some of them are planted in pots on the windowsill!			
W	Who's up for some **WINDOW SHOPPING**? Running out of pocket money doesn't mean you can't go to the shops! You can still look around and try things on.			
X	Visit an **EXHIBITION OR MUSEUM**! Lots of them are also free to visit, which means you can save your money for the gift shop.			
Y	Have a **YARD SALE**! I make a pile of clothes, books and games I don't want anymore. Then, with help from Mama, we display them on a table in the front garden, and open our own 'shop'!			
Z	**ZZZZZZZ**! I usually get up bright and early to make the most of Saturday and Sunday, but once in a while, it's brilliant to just snuggle down under the duvet.			

Fabulously fashionable word search

I'm crazy about clothes, and just as bonkers about cute accessories! See how many of my fashion favourites you can find hidden in this giant word search. Draw a loopy ring around each word when you find it, then cross it off on the list, too.

```
I D L E G W A R M E R S T L B
B U E O R T S H I R T J I V O
A N S F E G H A N D B A G C B
C G O C T I O T I C S H C B
K A R U I B R T S E A K T O L
P R V T A R T B K J N E S W E
A E E E R A S E I B D T T B H
C E A C A C R L R K A E R O A
K S C A P E M I T J L V A Y T
F L I P F L O P S E S N I B P
D O Q B N E C K L A C E N O S
R V E S T T O P H N Y E E O C
F X H A I R B O W S V T R T A
S G B G P A R T Y D R E S S R
K N E E S O C K S W T Z U S F
```

12

legwarmers

cute cap

mini skirt

flip flops

knee socks

cape

jeans

handbag

shorts

t-shirt

sandals

hair bow

scarf

necklace

tights

bracelet

jacket

bobble hat

tiara

trainers

party dress

cowboy boots

backpack

dungarees

vest top

Sporting superstars

One of my favourite things to do on a sunny afternoon is to set up a mini sports day. On your marks, get set, go!

Where to play?

Your back garden is the perfect spot for a sports day event, but if you haven't got a garden, the local park is just as good. Just make sure that you get permission from a parent or guardian.

Draw the line

Use chalk to draw out the start and finish line for your races, or stretch out a piece of rope to mark them instead.

Keeping score

Pick a member of your group to keep a note of who wins each race. That way, you can work out an overall sports day champion at the end.

Refreshments

You need lots of energy for all that racing around, so have some glasses of water or juice ready for competitors to drink, and maybe some fruit to snack on, too.

And the winner is . . .

Gather up some coloured card and cut out rosettes or medals for the winner.

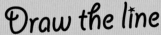

Events

Tug of love

You will need:
A long piece of rope
A pink ribbon
String

How to play:
Tie your pink ribbon to the middle of the rope, then split your competitors into two even teams. Mark two lines on the ground with string, around two metres apart. Position the rope so that the ribbon is in the middle of the two lines. Each team should then take one end of the rope and start pulling as hard as they can. The winning team is the one who manages to pull the ribbon over their line first.

You will need:
Scarves or strips of material
How to race:
Ask competitors to get into pairs and stand side by side. The person on the left should tie their right leg to the other person's left leg, using a scarf or piece of material. When the race begins, each pair of pals must race towards the finish line with their legs tied together and their arms around each other's waist.

SILVER

GOLD

BRONZE

Cuddly toy and spoon race

You will need:
Spoons
Small cuddly toys
How to race:
Give each competitor a spoon and a small cuddly toy. Ask them to balance the toy on the spoon. When you start the race, they should run as fast as they can, balancing the toy on the spoon, towards the finish line. Anyone who drops their toy must pick it up before carrying on.

Shopping trolley dash

Ask competitors to get together in pairs and decide who will be the shopper and who will be the trolley. Standing behind the start line, the 'trolley' players should put their hands on the ground, and let the 'shopper' grab their legs. When the dash starts, each pair has to race to the end with the 'trolleys' moving along on their hands, and the 'shoppers' guiding them from behind. The first pair over the finish line wins.

	Winner	Second place	Third place
Tug of love			
Best friends race			
Cuddly toy and spoon race			
Shopping trolley dash			

Lots of luck

Everyone needs a little bit of luck sometimes. Check out this lucky list for the month you were born in, then see if the special number, colour, flower or charm can add some extra luck to your life!

January
Lucky number: 7
Lucky colour: Aqua blue
Lucky flower: Snowdrop
Lucky charm: Acorn

February
Lucky number: 4
Lucky colour: Apple green
Lucky flower: Tulip
Lucky charm: Star

March
Lucky number: 12
Lucky colour: Cherry red
Lucky flower: Primrose
Lucky charm: Penny

April
Lucky number: 1
Lucky colour: Peach
Lucky flower: Daffodil
Lucky charm: Horseshoe

May
Lucky number: 21
Lucky colour: Yellow
Lucky flower: Sweet pea
Lucky charm: Heart

June
Lucky number: 3
Lucky colour: White
Lucky flower: Sunflower
Lucky charm: Four-leaf clover

July
Lucky number: 8
Lucky colour: Bubblegum pink
Lucky flower: Daisy
Lucky charm: Ladybird

August
Lucky number: 2
Lucky colour: Lavender
Lucky flower: Poppy
Lucky charm: Key

September
Lucky number: 17
Lucky colour: Magenta
Lucky flower: Marigold
Lucky charm: Snowflake

October
Lucky number: 5
Lucky colour: Midnight blue
Lucky flower: Rose
Lucky charm: Black cat

November
Lucky number: 11
Lucky colour: Tangerine orange
Lucky flower: Lily
Lucky charm: Anchor

Lucky tips

★ If you're nervous about a tricky test or exam, try wearing your lucky colour for some extra confidence!

★ Make yourself (or a friend) a bracelet threaded with beads in your lucky colour.

★ Look out for cute things featuring your lucky charm – for example, a rainbow notebook, a horseshoe necklace or a heart-patterned top.

17

Style by season

It's so much fun planning outfits for different times of the year. Whether it's finding something to suit the weather or dressing up for a special occasion, my wardrobe usually has the answer! Read the clues below and write the correct month next to each outfit.

January
Clue: The fluffy trim on this outfit keeps me cosy when it snows.

February
Clue: Hearts are the perfect look for Valentine's Day. Swoon.

March
Clue: It's lovely to wear green at the beginning of spring.

April
Clue: A cute umbrella and a raincoat make April showers tons of fun!

May
Clue: Old clothes and a floppy hat are just the thing for planting flowers in the garden.

June
Clue: Shorts, flip-flops and a comfy T-shirt are my summer holiday essentials!

July
Clue: Phew! My favourite swimsuit is perfect for cooling off at the hottest time of year.

August
Clue: Apples and polka dots make the cutest outfit for late summer days!

September
Clue: Smart dress and a new backpack? It's back-to-school time!

October
Clue: Don't be spooked – it's just me, dressing up for trick or treating!

November
Clue: Cool, crisp days mean jacket, jeans and a stylish scarf.

December
Clue: A Santa hat makes the cutest finishing touch to any outfit at this time of year!

What's your superstar name?

Have you ever wondered what you'd be called if you were a world-famous actress or singer? Mimmy and I love making up glamorous stage names for each other, and then practising our celebrity autographs! Use this brilliant chart to work out your own superstar stage name, then do it for your friends, too.

How it works

Find the first letter of your first name in the chart, and write down (or remember) the name next to it. Then check the first letter of your surname, and do the same. Add the two names together, and – ta da! – you're a superstar!

Real Name: Mimmy White
Superstar name:
Pixie Sparkles

Real name: Kitty White
Superstar name: Cherry Sparkles

If your first name begins with:

Then your superstar first name is:

If your surname begins with:

Then your superstar surname is:

	First name		Surname
A	Emerald	A	Diamond
B	Fairy	B	Sprinkles
C	Melody	C	Shimmer
D	Tiara	D	Angel
E	Trixie	E	Honey
F	Lucky	F	Heart
G	Silver	G	Cupcake
H	Blossom	H	Valentine
I	Fancy	I	Sapphire
J	London	J	Butterfly
K	Cherry	K	Candy
L	Tutu	L	Glitterbug
M	Pixie	M	Star
N	Rainbow	N	Princess
O	Lulu	O	Sunflower
P	Cookie	P	Daisy
Q	Luna	Q	Feather
R	Petal	R	Paris
S	Coco	S	Pearl
T	Zizi	T	Buttercup
U	Sequin	U	Skipper
V	Misty	V	Firefly
W	Moon	W	Sparkles
X	Bunny	X	Strawberry
Y	Pastel	Y	Darling
Z	Jewel	Z	Cool

Write yours here!

Real name: ....

....

Superstar name: ....

....

Now, practise your super-celeb autograph:

....

21

Super swap shop

It's official: swapping is cool! As well as being a brilliant way to try out new looks, books, movies and games, it's also environmentally-friendly and totally free! Get together with some friends and give it a go.

Getting started

Look around your bedroom and gather up anything you don't wear, read, listen to, watch or play with any more. Put everything in a pile and then check with a parent or guardian that it's OK for you to swap the things you've chosen. Done? Cool! Now, get your friends to do exactly the same in their bedrooms.

Making plans

Next, you'll need to choose a date, time and place for your swapping. Saturday afternoons are my favourite time, and it's a good idea to allow at least two or three hours. When it comes to the best place, pick somewhere with plenty of room so you can spread everything out. Living rooms are usually great or, if it's a sunny day, take your swap shop out into the garden instead.

Important tip: Make sure it's **VERY** clear which items are swappable, and which aren't. For instance, you might want to move your dad's film collection out of the living room, or put a big sign on your family bookshelves saying 'not for swapping'!

22

Take a token

To make sure your swappers leave with as much as they brought, you might want to give out tokens. These can just be little pieces of paper. When your guests arrive, give them one token for each item they've brought along. They can then use these like money, handing one over every time they want to 'buy' something from the pile of swaps to take home.

Tip: If there are just a few of you swapping, you can always leave this step out, and agree between you who gets to take home which goodies!

Tip: Use your bedroom or bathroom as a changing room for people to try on clothes away from the main swapping area.

Setting up shop

Arrange the things you want to swap in separate areas – keep clothes, accessories, books, toys, CDs and DVDs in different places so they don't get jumbled up. Ask guests to add their swaps to the right pile or area when they arrive.

Food and drink

You're bound to be hungry after all that swapping, so offer everyone something tasty while you sit around and chat about your cool new stuff. I love serving simple things like popcorn and yummy fruit salad. Keep them away from your 'shop' though – spill alert!

What's left?

There are usually at least a few things left over once everyone's taken what they want. Check that everyone's happy for you to donate them to a good cause, then ask a grown-up to drop them off at your local charity shop.

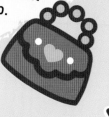

Hello Kitty's headscratchers

Put your brain power to the test with these clever quizzes.

All mixed up

Unscramble the letters in each group to spell out six of my very favourite things.

1. C O T L H E S
2. M S U I C
3. F D E I R N S
4. H O I L A Y D S
5. C P U C K A E S

Snap!

Only two of these photos are exactly the same. Can you spot them?

a

b

c

d

e

Odd one out

Can you spot the odd one out in each group of pictures?

a

b

c

I can count

....

bows.

Make more words

How many words can you make using just the letters in my name?
(I've added a few to get you started!)

HELLO KITTY   Key   Hit   Tie   Little

....

....

....

....

Tip: Carry on writing on a separate piece of paper if you run out of space.

10-20 words:
Well done, that's brilliant!
21-30 words:
Congratulations, you're awesome!
Over 31 words:
Wow, you're a total genius!

Changing rooms

My bedroom is where I do my homework, hang out with friends, practise dance routines, play games, plan all of my coolest outfits and, of course, fall asleep every night! With so much going on, I like to make sure the room looks its best. These are my favourite mini-makeover ideas. Why not try a few out for yourself?

Important: Make sure you ask a parent or guardian before you start!

Pretty pillows

Instead of buying new pillowcases, give your old ones a new look (make sure to check with your parents first!). Buy a pot of fabric paint and tip a little out on to an old plate. Then dip a heart-shaped eraser into the paint and use it to stamp colourful hearts all over the pillowcase material. So cute!

Happy hangers

Instead of keeping all your clothes hidden away inside the wardrobe, hang one up on the wall like a piece of art! Decorate a plain coat hanger with stickers, glitter, sequins or scraps of pretty material, then use it to show off your coolest dress or prettiest top.

Picture this

Make a collage of your favourite pictures, photos or mementoes. Glue them all on to a large piece of paper and display it on your wall. The picture can remind you of happy times or be something to inspire you to get even more creative!

DIY drawers

Add some sparkle to your furniture by covering drawer knobs or door handles with glitter! Ask a grown-up to unscrew them, then carefully brush on a coat of PVA glue. Sprinkle glitter over the glue, allow to dry, then ask a grown-up to screw the handles back into place. So gorgeous!

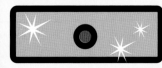

Snap!

Whether it's snapping pics on holiday or getting my pals to pose when we're hanging out at home, taking photographs is one of my very favourite things to do. Check out a few of these cool tips, and have a shot at taking some amazing photos of your own!

Cool cameras

It really doesn't matter what sort of camera you have – anyone can take great photos! Sometimes Papa lets me borrow his fancy camera, but often I just use my own small one or even the camera on my phone. With a bit of practice (and some top tips) they all work brilliantly!

Get moving

If you take all your photos standing in the same spot, they can start to look a bit boring. How about lying down? Now try snapping it from high up, or sideways on. It doesn't matter what you're photographing, it's always worth moving around and trying different angles.

No big shakes

Shaky or blurry pics can be really annoying! For nice, sharp snaps, you need to keep your camera as still as possible. To do this, tuck your elbows in against the sides of your body and hold the camera firmly in both hands. Take a nice deep breath just before you press the camera button. Easy peasy!

Prints charming

Although it's brilliant to store photos on your phone or computer, printing them out is lots more fun! I love popping my favourites into a cute frame, adding them to my scrapbook or fixing them to the notice-board in my bedroom.

Shoot it!

On holiday, I love taking pictures of the places we visit and the things we see, and sometimes even the food we eat. I love taking photos of a new outfit, a fun afternoon with my pals or even just a pretty flower in the garden.

Fake-a-booth

Why not set up your own mini-photobooth at home? All you need is a plain wall as your background, and a chair in front of it for your friends to sit on. Get them to sit close together, then say 'cheese' as you snap away! For a super-realistic effect, ask a grown-up to help you arrange the photos in a strip – just like real photobooth photos!

Say cheese!

Tip: Try using silly props, like hats, sunglasses and fake flowers, to make your fake-a-booth even more fun!

What's your dream holiday?

Are you a snow-bunny or a beach babe? A big-city shopper or an outdoor adventurer? Take this fun quiz and find out!

1.

What's your favourite kind of animal?
a) Peacock.
b) Penguin.
c) Dolphin.
d) Pony.

2.

On Sundays, you can usually be found:
a) Shopping with friends.
b) Snuggled up on the sofa at home.
c) At the swimming pool.
d) Having fun in your local park.

3.

Which three words would your friends use to describe you?
a) Fashionable, clever, confident.
b) Cute, friendly, outgoing.
c) Calm, girly, cheerful.
d) Fun, daring, lively.

4.

When it comes to cooking, you're best at:
a) Creating fabulous sandwich fillers.
b) Baking delicious treats, like cakes and cookies.
c) Making huge fruit salads and scrummy smoothies.
d) Helping out with family barbecues.

5.

Which accessory do you wear the most?
a) Your super-stylish sunglasses.
b) Your cute and cosy striped scarf.
c) Your fabulous, flower-trimmed straw hat.
d) Your totally trendy trainers.

Results

Mostly a)s:
Your perfect holiday hang-out would be a big city like Paris or New York. You love bright lights and busy streets, as well as going on sightseeing trips, visiting cool museums and window-shopping at amazing stores.

Mostly b)s:
You'd be super-happy visiting anywhere with lots of snow. From skiing, snowboarding and throwing snowballs, to snuggling up in your cosy chalet with cocoa and marshmallows. It's the perfect mix of indoor and outdoor fun!

Mostly c)s:
Your dream holiday would include blue skies, beautiful beaches and plenty of palm trees. You're happy on the beach or splashing about in the sea, and you've got the cutest collection of swimsuits for both! Just don't forget the sunscreen!

Mostly d)s
You'd be happiest on an action-packed adventure holiday. You love trying new activities and exploring, whether it's sleeping out on a cool camping trip, following an amazing nature trail or having fun at a wild and crazy theme park!

How do you doodle?

Some people believe that they can tell all sorts of things about you just by looking at your handwriting and your doodles. It's amazing! Check out my fun guide to discover just what your notes and scribbles mean.

So, what is a doodle?

A doodle is a little drawing you do without really thinking about it. My notepad is often covered with doodles after I've been chatting on the phone!

What your doodles mean

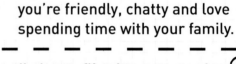 ★ If you doodle flowers it means you're friendly, chatty and love spending time with your family.

★ If you doodle butterflies it means you've got an amazing imagination and are probably a bit of a daydreamer!

★ If you doodle hearts it means you're kind, caring and thoughtful.

★ If you doodle your initials it means you love being the centre of attention.

★ If you doodle stars it means you've got bags of energy and you like to win!

 ★ If you doodle smiley faces it means you're cheerful and love to be surrounded by pretty things.

★ If you doodle birds it means you like making new friends and visiting new places.

 ★ If you doodle squares or triangles it means you're clever, confident and good at solving problems.

What your handwriting says about you

I love Hello Kitty   I love Hello Kitty

★ Look at a whole page of your writing. If it slants upwards, you're cheerful, honest and confident. If it slants downwards, you're conscientious and kind.

I love Hello Kitty   ## I love Hello Kitty

★ If your handwriting is small, it means you're clever and good at organising things. Big handwriting means you're a confident, friendly chatterbox.

Hello

★ Letters which are round and curvy mean you're arty, creative and good at things like music, drama or dancing.

Kitty

★ Spiky or pointed letters mean you're hard-working, super-smart and love learning new things.

Hello

★ If your letters are loopy or swirly, you're friendly and have an amazing imagination!

i i

★ Do you draw a little circle over the letter 'i' instead of a dot? Then you're probably girly, giggly and lots of fun!

t

★ Uh-oh – a long cross on the letter 't' means you're totally enthusiastic, but you can be a bit bossy, too!

O O

★ How do you write the letter 'o'? If it's big and open, you're a great pal and a bit of a chatterbox. A smaller, narrow 'o' means you're quiet, thoughtful and brilliant at keeping secrets.

Cheeky chequers

Chequers, or draughts, is a cool board game for two players. Mimmy and I have loads of fun challenging each other to matches, especially on rainy afternoons and long car journeys. It's really easy, so grab a pal and start playing!

• Counters •

Each player needs twelve counters. These can be counters from another board game you might have, or you can make them from scraps of card. Use a different colour for each person so you can tell easily which counters belong to which player.

Tip: You could cut out plain card circles to use as your counters, but for a special Hello Kitty version of the game, why not use two of these super-cute templates instead?

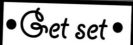

Younger Hello Kitty fans should always ask an adult to help them before using scissors or anything sharp.

• Get set •

Place the board on a flat surface, and sit opposite each other with the board in between you both. Place your counters on the side of the board nearest to you, adding them to the pink squares only.

• How to play •

- ✦ The aim of the game is to remove all your opponent's counters from the board.
- ✦ To start with, you can only move each counter diagonally forwards, which means sticking to the pink squares. You can only move on to empty squares.
- ✦ If the other player has a counter in front of yours with an empty square on the other side of it, then you can jump over the counter into the empty square and 'capture' the counter. This means that you take it off the board and keep it on your side of the table. Remember, you can only move diagonally forwards, even when you're jumping.

- ✦ When one of your counters makes it all the way across the board to the back row, it turns into a Princess. Hurrah! The other player has to take one of the counters they've captured from you and place it on top of the princess piece, like a crown. (If they haven't captured any of your counters, then leave your Princess where it is until they have.)
- ✦ Princess pieces can still only travel diagonally around the board, but now they can move backwards and forwards on the pink squares.

Tip: Start by putting your counters on the squares with a star in the middle.

Did you know? Chequerboards are usually black and white, but I think pink and red are much prettier!

• Game over •

The game ends when one of the players takes their turn, but can't move a counter. This is usually because the counters have all been captured, but – if you're super-smart – it might also be because you've blocked off all the squares they could move to! Either way, the player who can't move is the loser and the other person wins.

35

Fashion designer

Uh-oh! Something strange is going on in my wardrobe. There are plenty of cute outfits, but they're all looking seriously plain! Grab your favourite colouring pens, and add some fabulous patterns or designs.

Princess

Checks and plaid are perfect all year round!

Diagonal lines look cool on fun, punky outfits!

Zig-zags are awesome!

Add stars to make your design sparkle!

Polka dots and tiny spots are the cutest!

Simple stripes are a summer favourite!

Seriously spooked

Teddy is lost in this seriously spooky maze. See if you can help me rescue him without getting caught up in any cobwebs, and then find the way out!

This way

Way out

Build a blanket den

When the weather's cold and wet, or if I'm feeling a bit bored, building a den indoors is one of my favourite things to do! It's cute, cosy and the best kind of fun, whether you're hanging out with a few friends or snuggling up inside on your own.

Make sure you get permission from a parent or guardian before making your den.

Den DIY

A blanket den is a bit like a tent, only much easier to set up! To build a 'frame' around the outside, arrange chairs, tables, or any other bits of furniture in a square or circle shape. Make sure you allow plenty of space in the middle, and a gap to act as the entrance to your den. Next, gather up some sheets, blankets or duvets and hang them over the furniture. The ones over the top will make a roof for your den, and those hanging down at the sides will be the walls.

Tip: Don't forget to check with a grown-up before you start moving furniture to build your den. If you're lucky, they might even help you!

Make a seat

Once your den is built, it's time to start adding some goodies inside. Start with a pile of cushions and pillows so you have a nice squishy surface to sit on. Beanbags are really cool, too!

Lovely

Dens are often
it's a good idea t
torches ins

Hee!
Hee!
Hee!

Things to do

You can do just about anything inside your den! When I'm on my own, I love reading magazines, listening to music, making bead jewellery and watching films on Papa's laptop. Mimmy and I like playing board games too, but if there are a few of us hanging out, it's just as much fun to sit around chatting and giggling!

Snacks and drinks

Stock up your den with some tasty treats or even an indoor picnic. Try slurping your drinks from bottles instead of glasses, so they won't spill if you knock them over, and keep your snacks in bowls or containers instead of on plates.

WATER

HK

HK

Sleepover style

Sometimes, Mama and Papa let me sleep inside one of my dens, and it's my favourite kind of sleepover! Mimmy and I drag our sleeping bags inside, with some books for bedtime reading. If we have friends staying over, we always tell a few spooky stories before falling asleep, too!

Spot the difference

Hmmm, there's something strange about these holiday snaps. Can you spot six differences between each pair of pictures?

Queensway STOP

Queensway GO

Tea party time

Tea parties are fancy and fun! Find out how to throw your own with my top tea-time tips.

Make sure you get permission from a parent or guardian before planning your tea party.

Set the table

Cover your table with a nice, smart tablecloth, or a plain sheet if you don't have a cloth. Add a tea-plate for each guest, plus a cup and saucer. Even if you prefer juice to actual tea, it's still fun to drink it from a cute teacup! For added fanciness, fold some napkins and add a vase or glass jar full of pretty flowers.

Cake stand DIY

Cakes and sandwiches look brilliant when they're displayed on a super-stylish cake stand. Don't worry if you haven't got one, though – you can make a fun DIY version instead! Start with a big paper or plastic plate, and glue a paper or plastic cup in the middle. Glue a medium-sized plate on top of the cup, then add another cup on top of that. Finish off with a small plate at the very top. Leave the glue to dry overnight, then fill your fancy cake-stand with tasty snacks!

Sandwich fillings

Make your sandwiches from thinly-sliced bread, cut into narrow rectangles or tiny triangles. Trim the crusts off to make them look even more posh! These are some of my favourite tea-party fillings:

★ Egg and cress
★ Honey and grated cheese
★ Cream cheese and strawberry jam (pink sandwiches!)
★ Tuna and cucumber
★ Tomato, basil and cream cheese
★ Peanut butter and jam

Important: Always ask a grown-up to help you in the kitchen.

Sweet stuff

As well as sandwiches, I love serving up a few sweet treats. French fancies, scones, mini-muffins and small fruits, such as berries, are my absolute favourites!

Dressing up

Tea parties are the perfect excuse to wear your prettiest outfit! I love choosing a cute dress and adding some fun accessories. In the winter, it might be a sweet cardigan and patterned tights, and in the summer, a flowery hair-clip and my sparkly sandals. Ask your guests to dress up too, so you all feel extra-special as you have your tea!

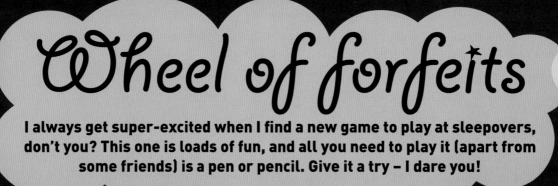

Wheel of forfeits

I always get super-excited when I find a new game to play at sleepovers, don't you? This one is loads of fun, and all you need to play it (apart from some friends) is a pen or pencil. Give it a try – I dare you!

In a spin

To make a pointer for your wheel of forfeits, place this book down on a flat surface and rest a pen or pencil on top of the coloured circle. Hold the pen or pencil in the middle, and give it a little flick so it spins around on the page. The sharp end, or pointer, should land in just one of the sections each time.

Tip: It's fine to change some of the forfeits if you need to. For instance, if you haven't got a spoon, try replacing that section with a totally tricky forfeit of your own!

How to play

★ Before each turn, a player has to tell the group whether they want to try for a pink forfeit (worth two points) or a yellow one (worth three points). They then spin the pointer. When it stops spinning, the player has to do one of the forfeits in the section it's pointing to.

★ Players are not allowed to change their mind about the colour they've picked after spinning! They can say 'pass' if they don't want to do the forfeit, but this loses points.

★ If the pointer lands on a 'lucky escape', the player earns their points without having to do a forfeit.

★ Keep playing, taking it in turns to spin and perform your forfeits. The winner is the first player to score over twenty points.

Scoring

★ Each player scores two points for every pink forfeit completed, and three points for every yellow forfeit. They also score two points for a pink 'lucky escape' and three for a yellow 'lucky escape'.

★ If a player says 'pass' after choosing a pink forfeit, they lose two points. If they pass on a yellow forfeit, they lose three points.

Pink (two point) forfeits

1. Hold your nose and hop around the room in a circle.
2. Balance a spoon on your nose for ten seconds.
3. Do an impression of a character from the last film you saw.
4. Play air guitar or drums for 30 seconds.
5. Make three people in the room laugh.
6. Stand on one leg for 30 seconds.

Yellow (three point) forfeits

1. Sing the words of your favourite song to the tune of 'Happy Birthday'.
2. Say the alphabet backwards while balancing on one leg.
3. Pretend to be a monkey at a ballet class.
4. Talk about shoes for a whole minute without stopping.
5. Sing a TV show theme like you were an opera singer.
6. Say 'Hello Kitty threw three free throws' five times in ten seconds.

forfeit 6

forfeit 1

forfeit 5

lucky escape

forfeit 6

forfeit 1

lucky escape

forfeit 2

forfeit 5

lucky escape

forfeit 4

forfeit 3

lucky escape

forfeit 2

forfeit 4

forfeit 3

Be cute, go green!

Everyone knows it's good to be green and take care of the planet, but did you know green can be seriously cute, too? Take a peek at some of my favourite eco-friendly tips!

Totes amazing

Carry a trendy tote instead of using plastic bags when you're out shopping. I bought a plain one which was super-cheap, then customised it with sequins and buttons. It's a hundred times greener than a carrier bag and a million times more adorable!

Bye-bye bottles

Use a cute flask instead of buying bottles of water or juice. I've got one with a cool star pattern and Mimmy has a flowery one! As well as being greener than throwing away plastic bottles every day, it also means we can take all sorts of different drinks to school, from fruit juice and squash to homemade smoothies.

Pretty pots

Re-use empty, clean glass food jars to hold flowers, coins, pens, hair accessories or other bits and pieces in your bedroom. I love wrapping strips of ribbon or fancy fabric around the jar first, so it's pretty as well as useful!

In the bin

Make a special waste bin for your bedroom! I found an old, plain one and decorated it with green paint and sparkly glitter. Fill it with things like old notes, and magazines you've finished reading, then add the paper to your family recycling each week.

Fabulous fruit and veggies

Grow your own tasty treats instead of buying them in the shops. Herby bread or scrummy strawberry shortcakes taste even more amazing when you've grown the ingredients in your garden or on a windowsill. Add some flower seeds when you're planting too, so you can have pretty blossoms for a vase, or even to pin in your hair!

Garden

No blow

Save electricity by letting your hair dry naturally instead of blow-drying. Try tying it in plaits, then shaking them out when it's dry for a fun and totally gorgeous wavy look!

What's your perfect party?

When it comes to parties, there are so many fun types to choose from. If you need help making up your mind, try this cool quiz and find out which party is perfect for you!

1.

You're the kind of friend who:
a) Is super-popular and gives the best makeovers ever!
b) Gives great advice and always gets people giggling!
c) Is kind, caring and never forgets anyone's birthday!
d) Is brilliant fun and always arranges cool days out!

2.

What's your favourite time of year?
a) Summer – it's the perfect excuse to wear sunglasses all the time.
b) Winter – chilly days are the best for snuggling up with a good book.
c) Spring – you love all the pretty flowers and new baby animals.
d) Autumn – playing in all those crunchy leaves is so much fun.

3.

You love snacking on:
a) Fancy crisps and sparkling lemonade.
b) Popcorn and mini-pizzas.
c) Strawberries and cupcakes.
d) Hamburgers and salad.

4.

What would your dream bedroom be like?
a) Glitzy and glamorous with a huge wardrobe and lots of posters on the walls.
b) Sleek and stylish with a cool computer desk and plenty of book shelves.
c) Pastel pink with fluffy rugs, pretty curtains and lots of cosy cushions.
d) Simple and laid-back with a big TV and an even bigger games cupboard.

5.

If you won an award, it would probably be:
a) A Best Actress Oscar (thank you, darlings)!
b) A smart medal for writing the best story in class.
c) A cute Friend of the Year cup.
d) The school Sports Day trophy.

Mostly a)s

Woo-hoo! You should totally throw a groovy dance party. You're confident, fashionable and love being the centre of attention. Dancing is one of your favourite hobbies, especially when it means you get to wear something sparkly and hang out under a party glitter ball!

Mostly b)s

Yay! You should definitely try a cool movie-screening party. You're stylish and clever with a brilliant sense of humour. You love stories, whether they're in books or on a movie screen, especially when you get to giggle along with your friends!

Mostly c)s

Aw! You should set up a super-cute sleepover. You're sweet, girly and love anything pink or fluffy. Hanging out with your friends is one of your favourite things in the world, especially when it means you get to swap secrets all night long!

Mostly d)s

Hurrah! You should go for a fun-and-games birthday bash. You're sporty and outgoing with bags of energy. You love being silly and trying new things, especially when there's the chance to win a cool prize at the end!

Turn the page to read about my all-time favourite party games!

Best-ever party games

I love so much about parties – the dressing up, the dancing, the yummy party food . . . but what I really look forward to is playing some fun games! These are a few of my all-time favourites. Why not give them a go at your next bash?

Hello Kitty says

Pick a person to be 'Hello Kitty' and have them stand in front of everyone else. They then tell everyone else what to do, for instance, 'Hello Kitty says stand on one leg'. Everyone in the room has to do what Hello Kitty says, until they leave out the phrase 'Hello Kitty says'. So, for example, if they say, 'Stick out your tongue', you shouldn't do that. If they say, 'Hello Kitty says stick out your tongue', you should definitely stick it out! Anyone who fails to do something 'Hello Kitty says', or does it when there's no 'Hello Kitty says' is out. The winner is the last person left in the game.

Place the bow on Hello Kitty

Copy your favourite Hello Kitty picture from this book on to a piece of paper, but leave out the hair bow. Copy and cut out a separate bow from card, and fix a piece of sticky-tac to the back. One at a time, tie a scarf around each player's eyes so they're blindfolded. Spin them round three times, then ask them to put the bow on to Hello Kitty's head. The player who gets it closest to the right spot is the winner.

Younger Hello Kitty fans should always ask an adult to help them before using scissors or anything sharp.

Tip: At our parties, Mimmy and I give an extra prize to the person who gets the bow in the funniest wrong place!

52

Hello, Hello Kitty

Ask all of your players to sit in a circle, then pick someone to be the first 'tapper'. That player stands up and walks around the outside of the circle, tapping everyone on the head in turn. She says 'hello' with each head she taps and then, at random, changes this to 'Hello Kitty'. (So, for instance, she might tap four heads, saying 'hello, hello, hello, hello' and then say 'Hello Kitty' as she taps the fifth head.) As soon as she says this, the tapper has to change direction and run back around the circle to try and sit in the empty space. The 'Hello Kitty' has to jump up and run in the other direction to try and get to the space first. The loser – the person who gets to the empty space last – is the next tapper, and continues the game.

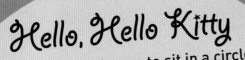

Musical strike a pose!

Choose someone to be your DJ, or ask a grown-up to do it for you. It's their job to start and stop the music, and be the judge. When the music starts, players dance around as wildly as they can. When it stops, everyone has to stop dancing and pull their best model pose. The last person to stop moving is out. The game carries on in the same way, and the winner is the last person left posing.

Hello cookies

What's totally tasty and absolutely adorable at the same time?
It's my delicious Hello Kitty cookies, of course!

Important!
★ Always ask a grown-up to help you in the kitchen.
★ Don't forget to wash your hands before you start cooking, and wear an apron to stop your clothes getting messy!

Cutie cutters

Before you start, copy or trace this template on to a piece of card (an old cereal box is perfect). Ask a grown-up to cut it out, then set aside until your cookie dough is rolled out and ready to go.

Recipe

You will need:
★ 225g butter or margarine
★ 175g caster sugar
★ Pinch of salt
★ 1 egg
★ 2 tsp vanilla extract
★ 300g plain flour
★ Currants or raisins
★ Tube of icing
★ Sprinkles

Butter

Flour

What to do:

1. Put the butter and sugar in a large bowl. Stir hard, using a wooden spoon, until they're completely mixed together.
2. Break the egg into the bowl, then add the salt and vanilla extract. Stir them into the butter and sugar.
3. Add the flour, then start stirring again until you've got a nice, firm dough. Use your hands if it gets too stiff to stir.
4. Place your dough in the fridge for 1-2 hours to chill.
5. Ask a grown-up to turn the oven on to 180°C (160°C fan oven / 350°F / gas mark 4).
6. When you're ready, sprinkle some extra flour on to your work surface. Add the dough on top, then roll it out with a rolling pin so it's about 5mm thick.
7. Place your cardboard cookie template on top and ask a grown-up to cut around the outside with a small knife.
8. When your grown-up has cut out as many cookies as they can from the rolled out dough, scrunch up the leftover pieces, and roll them out again.
9. Place your cookies on a non-stick baking sheet. Add currants or raisins to each one to make my eyes and nose.
10. Ask a grown-up to place the cookies in the oven for 10-12 minutes, until the edges are just starting to turn light brown. Ask a grown-up to take them out for you when they're done.
11. Leave the cookies until they're completely cool, then spread a little bit of icing over one side of my head to look like a bow. Add some sprinkles on top of the icing for a cute and colourful finishing touch!

Tip: I sometimes mix up the dough the day before I want to make my cookies. Mama lets me leave it in the fridge overnight, and then we roll it out and bake the cookies the next morning.

Favourite flavours

Try these delicious ideas to give your cookies a different taste.
★ Try adding some grated orange or lemon zest instead of the vanilla for a zingy, fruity flavour.
★ How about chocolate biscuits? Replace 50g of the flour with cocoa powder.

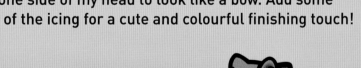

Red carpet race

My friends and I have been invited to a cool movie premiere. Can you help us get there in time? The first person to arrive on the red carpet is the winner!

You will need:
★ Counters, buttons or circles of coloured card
★ A die

How to play:
Each player chooses a different character and places a counter on the starting spot to play as that person. Players then take it in turns to throw the die and move the number of spaces shown. Remember to obey any instructions on the squares you land on!

start

1

2 Wow! Your outfit is amazing. Go forward 3 spaces.

3

25

24 The wind messes up your hair. Go back 2 spaces.

23

22

21

26

27

28

29 A celebrity snapper takes your photo! Go forward 1 space.

30

31

32

8

9 Oh, no! You've forgotten your invitation. Go back to the start.

10

11 See a poster advertising the film. Go forward 1 space.

7

12

6 Stop to put on some lip balm. Miss a turn.

15 Stop off to buy popcorn. Miss a turn.

13

16

5

14

17

4

18

37 Get some superstar autographs! Go forward 1 space

38

19 Oops! You trip over in your party shoes. Go back 1 space.

36

39

20

35

33 Cool – you've spotted your favourite film star! Go forward 3 spaces.

34

The red carpet!
You win!

What to do:

You will need:
★ One sheet of A4 paper
★ Scissors

Tip: Every time you fold the paper, make sure you press nice and firmly along the folded edge to make a sharp crease.

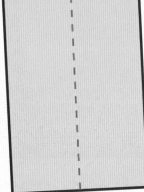

1. Fold the paper in half lengthways, then flatten it out again.

2. Fold the paper in half widthways.

3. Next, take the top layer of paper and fold the bottom edge up towards the centre crease.

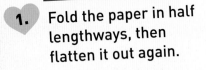

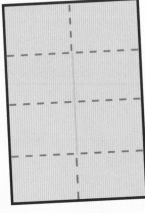

4. Flip the paper over, and fold the bottom layer of paper up towards the centre.

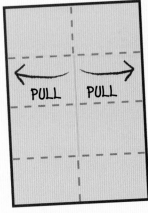

PULL   PULL

5. Flatten the whole sheet of paper out again. Ask an adult to cut along the two middle sections (the blue line on the diagram).

6. Hold the paper on each side of the cut, gripping the centre fold between your fingers and thumbs. Give it a gentle pull, and the folded sections should come together in a sort of cross shape.

Important: Younger Hello Kitty fans should ask an adult to help them with scissors.

7. Bring all four sections, or pages, together, and – ta da! – you've made a mini-book.

Fill it up!

It's totally up to you how you want to fill your mini book! Have a go at one of these suggestions or dream up some of your own.

Tip: It's heaps of fun to keep your mini-books, but they make brilliant presents for your friends and family, too.

★ Start your very own fashion magazine! Design some cool clothes, draw them on the pages, then add little scraps of fabric to show the materials you'd use to make them. You can add photos of some of your favourite outfits as well. Don't forget to strike a fashion model pose first!

★ Use a pen or pencil to draw a big '+' in the middle of each page, so it's split into four quarters, or boxes. Fill each one with words and pictures to create a cool comic book!

★ Write a short story and add some cute drawings to go with it. Use alphabet stickers to spell out your title on the front.

★ How about starting a fan magazine, all about your favourite band or singer? Fill it with plenty of pictures, your favourite song words, fun facts, and even autographs!

Hello Kitty
XX

★ Make a mini scrapbook, by sticking photos and souvenirs from a special event or occasion to the pages.

Answers

1. May; **2.** July; **3.** October;
4. December; **5.** November;
6. April; **7.** March; **8.** February;
9. June; **10.** August;
11. September; **12.** January.

ALL MIXED UP
1. Clothes; **2.** Music;
3. Friends; **4.** Holidays;
5. Cupcakes.
SNAP!
Pictures a and e are the same.
ODD ONE OUT
a. Star; **b.** Carrot;
c. Sunglasses.
BOW-TIFUL
There are 20 bows.